AGE
13–14
Key Stage 3

National Tests
practice papers

FOR THE YEAR 2004

Maths
Book 1 Levels 4–8

practice
papers

Contents	Page

First published 2003
exclusively for WHSmith by
Hodder & Stoughton Educational,
a division of Hodder Headline Ltd
338 Euston Road
London NW1 3BH

A CIP record for this book is available from the British Library.

Authors: Steve Mills and Hilary Koll

ISBN 0340 81386 5

Impression   5   4   3   2
Year   2004

Printed and bound by Graphycems, Spain

NOTE: The tests, questions and advice in this book are not reproductions of the official test materials sent to schools. The official testing process is supported by guidance and training for teachers in setting and marking tests and interpreting the results. The results achieved in the tests in this book may not be the same as are achieved in the official tests.

What are the National Tests?

Children who attend state schools in England and Wales sit National Tests (commonly known as SATs) at the ages of 7, 11 and 14, usually at the beginning of May. The test results are accompanied by an assessment by the child's teacher (at Key Stage 3 this also covers non-tested subjects such as History or Geography).

The results are used by the school to assess each child's level of knowledge and progress in English and Maths at Key Stage 1 and English, Maths and Science at Key Stages 2 and 3. They also provide guidance for the child's next teacher when he or she is planning the year.

The educational calendar for children aged 5–14 is structured as follows:

Key Stage	Year	Age by end of year	National Test
1 (KS1)	1	6	
	2	7	KEY STAGE 1
2 (KS2)	3	8	Optional Year 3
	4	9	Optional Year 4
	5	10	Optional Year 5
	6	11	KEY STAGE 2
3 (KS3)	7	12	
	8	13	
	9	14	KEY STAGE 3

Timetable

Key Stage 3 students will sit their tests on **4–7 May 2004** (check with the school as dates may change).

Levels

National targets have been set for children's results in the National Tests, as follows:

LEVEL	AGE 7	AGE 11	AGE 14
8			
7			
6			
5			
4			
3			
2			
2a			
2b			
2c			
1			

Below expected level   Above expected level

Expected level   Exceptional

What can parents do to help?

While it is never a good idea to encourage cramming, you can help your child to succeed by:

- Making sure he or she has enough food, sleep and leisure time during the test period.
- Practising important skills such as writing, spelling and mental arithmetic.
- Telling him or her what to expect in the test, such as important symbols.
- Helping him or her to be comfortable in test conditions including working within a time limit, reading questions carefully and understanding different ways of answering.

Introduction

Maths at Key Stage 3

The Key Stage 3 Maths Test consists of two written papers, one to be taken without a calculator and the other with a calculator, and a mental arithmetic test. The tests will cover aspects of Number and Algebra, Shape, Space and Measures, and Handling Data.

Levels and tiers of entry

For mathematics, your child will be entered for one of four tiers. Your child's teacher will make a judgement about which of the tiers to enter your child for, deciding on the tier that best matches his or her ability.

Tiers: Levels 3–5
         Levels 4–6
         Levels 5–7
         Levels 6–8.

An additional extension paper can be taken by children working at level 8 or beyond.

This book includes two written papers that cover the most popular tiers of entry. Paper 1 covers levels 4–6 and Paper 2 covers levels 5–7. Separate level 8 practice questions are included for those performing above the expected standard for 14-year-olds. The mental arithmetic test includes questions at levels 4–7.

To gain an idea of the level at which your child is working, use the table on page 57, which shows you how to convert your child's marks into a National Curriculum level.

Setting the Maths Tests

Equipment needed

Paper 1: pen, pencil, ruler, rubber.

Paper 2: pen, pencil, ruler, rubber, protractor or angle measurer, pair of compasses, scientific or graphic calculator, tracing paper, mirror (optional).

Mental Maths Test: pencil and rubber.

A clock or watch with a second hand is useful for ensuring times for each question on the mental test are appropriate. No extra paper is needed. Answers and working should be written in this book.

The written papers

A formula sheet is included for each test. Encourage your child to refer to it where necessary. Each written paper lasts for **1 hour**, starting with easier questions and gradually becoming more difficult.

The Mental Maths Test

The mental test should take approximately **20 minutes** to give. Cut out pages 47 to 48 so you can read them aloud to your child.

You will need to ensure that you read the questions to your child within the set times. Read each question twice. Your child should use the sheets on pages 44 to 46 to write his or her answers.

1 mark should be awarded for each correct answer.

Marking the tests

Next to each question in the written tests is a number indicating how many marks the question or part of the question is worth.

Enter your child's mark into the circle above, using the answer pages to help you decide how many points to award.

The answer pages (49–57) also offer advice, provide information about common errors made by pupils and include tips to help your child understand the mathematical ideas.

Find your child's total score from the written papers and refer to page 57 for information about the level at which your child might be working.

Whatever your child achieves, help him or her to feel positive and confident by giving plenty of praise for the efforts made.

You *cannot* use a calculator for any questions in Paper 1.

Formulae

You might need to use these formulae.

AREA

Circle

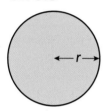

πr^2

Take π as 3.14.

Triangle

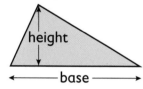

$$\dfrac{\text{base} \times \text{height}}{2}$$

Parallelogram

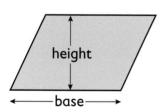

$\text{base} \times \text{height}$

Trapezium

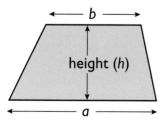

$$\dfrac{(a + b)}{2} \times h$$

LENGTH

Circle

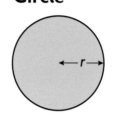

$\text{circumference} = 2\pi r$

VOLUME

Prism

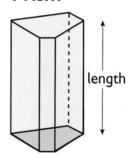

$\text{area of cross section} \times \text{length}$

You will need:
pen, pencil, rubber and ruler

Practice questions

Write one number in each box to make each equation correct.

Example

$112 + 60 = \boxed{\textbf{172}}$

a $129 + 80 = \boxed{}$

b $645 - 50 = \boxed{}$

c $100 - \boxed{} = 67$

d $\boxed{} \times \boxed{} = 800$

1 Write one number in each box to make each equation correct.

 a $12 \times \boxed{} = 1200$

1

 b $300 \div \boxed{} = 75$

1

 c $\boxed{} - 40 = 87$

1

 d $\boxed{} \times 7 = 210$

1

 e $\boxed{} \div \boxed{} = 12$

1

TOTAL

5

3

Ice-skating

2 Colin and Jane have entered an ice-skating competition.

There are five judges.

Each judge can give up to six marks.

Here are the marks Colin was given.

| 5.6 | 5.8 | 6.0 | 5.5 | 4.9 |

a Write these marks in order of size, starting with the smallest.

1

b Find the total number of marks Colin was given.

1

c Write a number that lies between | 5.6 | and | 5.5 |

Jane was given a total of **25.4** marks.

1

d What number is **10 times larger** than Jane's total?

1

TOTAL

4

3 Some children are racing snails.

These are their positions after a few minutes.

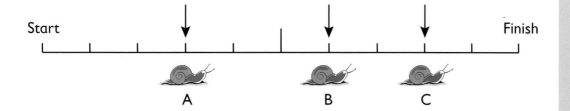

Start   A   B   C   Finish

a What fraction of the track has snail A travelled?

1

b What fraction of the track has snail B travelled?
Give your answer in its simplest form.

1

c What percentage of the track does snail C still have to travel to reach the finish line?

1

TOTAL

3

d If snail D has moved one third as far as snail B, mark a D on the track to show the position of snail D.

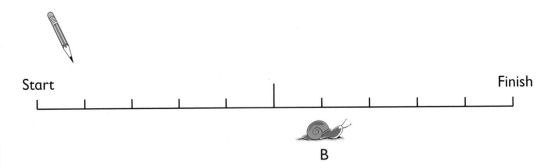

1

e Another snail is moving along a track.
It has moved $\frac{3}{5}$ of the way along the track.
Draw an arrow ↓ to show its position.

1

4 **a** A clothes shop is having a sale.

In the sale, pairs of socks are **£1.25** each.

What is the cost of **12** pairs of socks?

£

1

b The shop also sells T-shirts.

Each T-shirt costs **£4.49**.

How much would **3** T-shirts cost?

£

1

c Dave spends exactly **£11.48** on T-shirts and socks.

How many pairs of socks does Dave buy?

1

TOTAL

3

d Dave pays for his T-shirts and socks with a £20 note.

How much change does he get?

1

e Jennie decides to buy some T-shirts and socks for her friends at Christmas.

She has **£20** to spend.

What combinations of socks and T-shirts can she buy?

1

TOTAL

2

5 Using two identical tiles shaped like this:

we can put tiles together by joining **along sides**, like this:

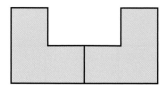 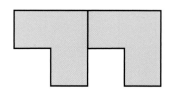

but not like this:

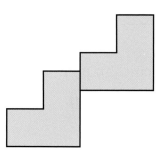 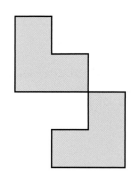

a Draw a **different shape** using two tiles joined together.

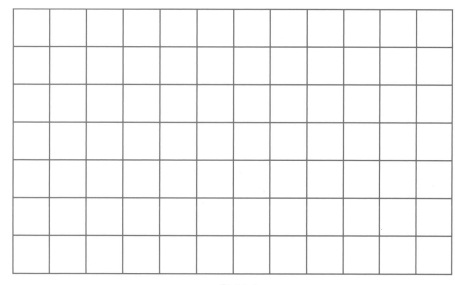

Grid 1

1

TOTAL

1

9

b Draw **another different shape** using two tiles.

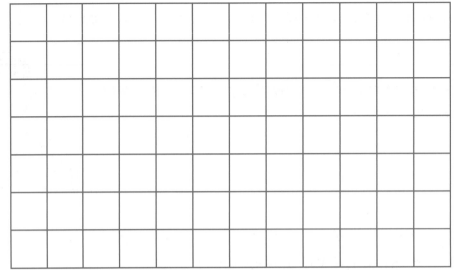

Grid 2

1

The sides of the squares on the grids are **1 cm long**.

c What is the perimeter of the shape you drew on **Grid 1**?

1

d What is the perimeter of the shape you drew on **Grid 2**?

1

TOTAL

3

10

6 James has taken all the **diamond** cards from a pack of playing cards. He removes the Jack, Queen and King cards, so that he now has **10 diamond** cards numbered from **1 to 10**.

He only uses these cards.

James shuffles the cards and picks one without looking.

a What is the **probability** that James picks the **4 of diamonds**? Write your answer as a **fraction**.

1

b Draw a cross on this line to show the probability that James picks the **8 of diamonds**.

impossible   certain

1

c Draw a cross on this line to show the probability that James picks a diamond card with a number **less than 5**.

impossible   certain

1

TOTAL

3

James decides to pick a card, write the number down and **put the card back**.

He does this **50 times**. He organises his results into a table.

Card number	Frequency
1	4
2	8
3	5
4	2
5	9
6	3
7	7
8	5
9	0
10	7

d James looks at his results and says:

"There is a greater probability of picking the number 5 than any other number."

Explain why James is **wrong**.

7 Safwan and Rosie played a game with the numbers in this grid.

4	−2	8
−6	−1	0

They took it in turns to choose two numbers from the grid and to find the **total**.

Safwan made the total **7**, by choosing the numbers **8** and **−1**.

a Rosie made the total **3**. Which two numbers did she choose?

1

b Safwan made the total **−2**. Which two numbers could he have chosen?

1

c There are two different ways of making the total **2**. Fill in the table to show the two ways.

Two numbers chosen	total
	2
	2

2

TOTAL

4

13

8 A square has **4 lines of reflective symmetry**

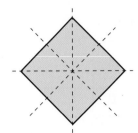

and has **rotational symmetry** of **order 4**.

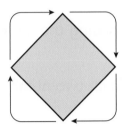

Here are some quadrilaterals.

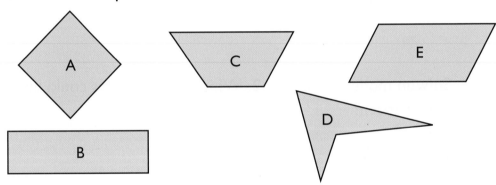

Fill in the missing numbers in the table below.

	lines of reflective symmetry	rotational symmetry of order
Shape A	4	4
Shape B		
Shape C		
Shape D		
Shape E		

4

TOTAL

4

14

9 Clare has some money in her purse.

Call the number of pence she has n.

a Clare takes out 10p from her purse.

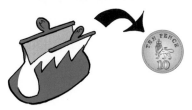

Write an expression to show how many pence are now in the purse.

....

1

b Clare puts the 10p back so that she starts again with n pence in her purse.

She takes out exactly **half** the money in the purse.

half

Write an expression to show how many pence are now in the purse.

....

1

TOTAL

2

Clare starts again with *n* pence in her purse.

c Clare's mum has exactly **100 times** as much money as this.

Write an expression to show how many pence Clare's mum has.

....

1

d Write an expression to show how many **pounds** Clare's mum has.

....

1

e These expressions show how many pence are in these two wallets.

Wallet A   Wallet B

2*n* + 4   2(*n* + 2)

Do the wallets hold the same amount?

Explain your answer.

1

TOTAL

3

10 a Mr Hicks runs at **16 kilometres per hour**.

During one month Mr Hicks ran a total of **220 kilometres**.

For approximately how many hours did he run?

Show your working.

2

b Yesterday Mr Hicks ran for $3\frac{3}{4}$ hours at **16 kilometres per hour**.

How many **kilometres** did he run yesterday?

1

c Mr Hicks runs at **16 kilometres per hour**.

Approximately how many **miles per hour** is this?

1

TOTAL

4

17

11 James has drawn a sketch of a building on a hillside.

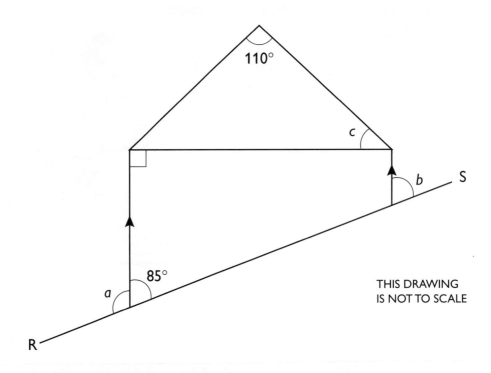

110°

c

b   S

85°

a

THIS DRAWING
IS NOT TO SCALE

R

The two vertical walls of the building are **parallel** and the drawing of the roof is an **isosceles triangle**. The line **RS** is a straight line.

Calculate angles *a*, *b* and *c*.

a = ... °

b = ... °

c = ... °

3

TOTAL

3

12 Here is a sequence of shapes made from white and coloured squares.

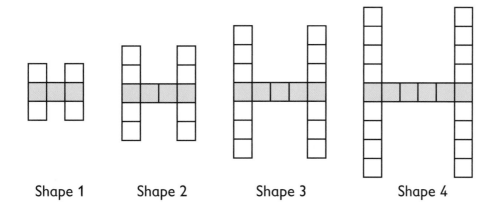

Shape 1   Shape 2   Shape 3   Shape 4

a Complete the table by filling in the missing numbers for Shape **8** and Shape **10**:

2

Shape number	1	2	3	4	8	10
Number of coloured squares	3	4	5	6		
Number of white squares	4	8	12	16		

b Complete the table by writing **expressions** for Shape *n*:

Shape number	1	2	3	4	*n*
Number of coloured squares	3	4	5	6	
Number of white squares	4	8	12	16	

2

TOTAL

4

19

c Write an expression to show the **total** number of squares used to make Shape **n**. **Simplify** your expression.

1

d For a different sequence of shapes the number of **triangles** used can be expressed as **4n + 2**.

Which of the sets of shapes below shows Shapes 2 and 3 in this sequence?

Set 1

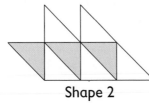

Shape 2

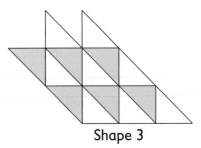

Shape 3

Set 2

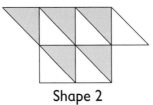

Shape 2

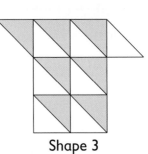

Shape 3

Set 3

Shape 2

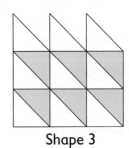

Shape 3

1

TOTAL

2

Set ....

13 Some straight lines have been drawn onto this co-ordinate grid
to make a pentagon that has **two** pairs of **parallel** sides.

One side of the pentagon has the equation $x = 8$. This side has
been drawn with a bold line and labelled.

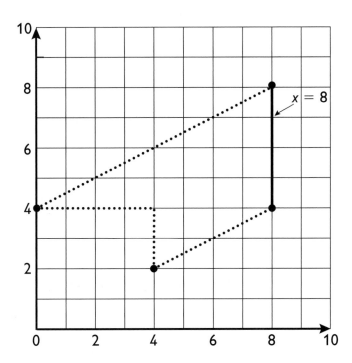

a **One** of the sides of the pentagon has the equation $y = 4$.

On the diagram above, draw over the side $y = 4$ with a
bold line and label it.

1

b The **longest** side of the pentagon has the equation
$y = \frac{1}{2}x + 4$.

What is the equation of the side parallel to this one?

1

TOTAL

2

21

14 a There are **20** pupils in a maths class. **12** of the pupils are boys.

The name of each pupil is written on a piece of paper and put in a box.

One of the names is chosen at random.

Tick the **five** values in the rectangle that show the **probability** that the name chosen is a boy's name.

12%	$\frac{12}{20}$	0.12	1.2	20%
0.6			60%	$\frac{12}{32}$
	$\frac{6}{10}$	$\frac{20}{12}$	0.06	$\frac{3}{5}$

There are **20** pupils in an English class.

The first name of **7** of the pupils begins with the letter S.

The name of each pupil is written on a piece of paper and put in a box.

One of the names is chosen at random.

What is the probability that the name chosen **does not** begin with the letter S?

b Write your answer as a fraction.

c Write your answer as a percentage.

2

1

1

TOTAL

4

22

15 Here are two shapes. They are <u>not</u> drawn to scale.

The area of the trapezium is **twice** the area of the parallelogram.

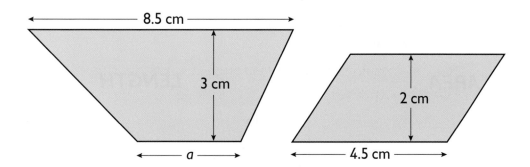

a Calculate the length of side *a*.

Show your working.

$a =$ .... cm

2

b What is the area of the trapezium below?

Give your answer in terms of *b*, in its simplest form.

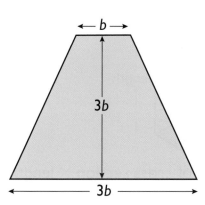

Area = ...

1

TOTAL

3

23

You *can* use a calculator for any questions in Paper 2.

Formulae

You might need to use these formulae.

AREA

Circle

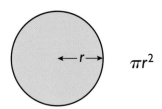

πr^2

Take π as 3.14 or use the π button on your calculator.

Triangle

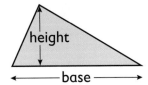

$\dfrac{\text{base} \times \text{height}}{2}$

Parallelogram

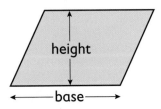

base $\times$ height

Trapezium

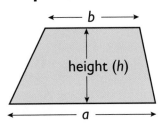

$\dfrac{(a + b)}{2} \times h$

LENGTH

Circle

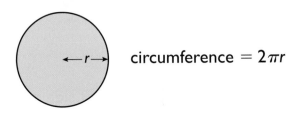

circumference $= 2\pi r$

For a right-angled triangle

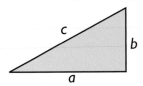

$a^2 + b^2 = c^2$ (Pythagoras' Theorem)

VOLUME

Prism

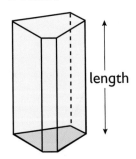

area of cross section $\times$ length

> *You will need:*
> pen, pencil, rubber, ruler, scientific or graphic calculator, protractor, tracing paper, a pair of compasses, a mirror (optional).

1 Shape X has been rotated in five different ways.

In each case, the rotated shape is labelled Shape Y.

a Draw a cross on each set of shapes to show the **centre of rotation**.

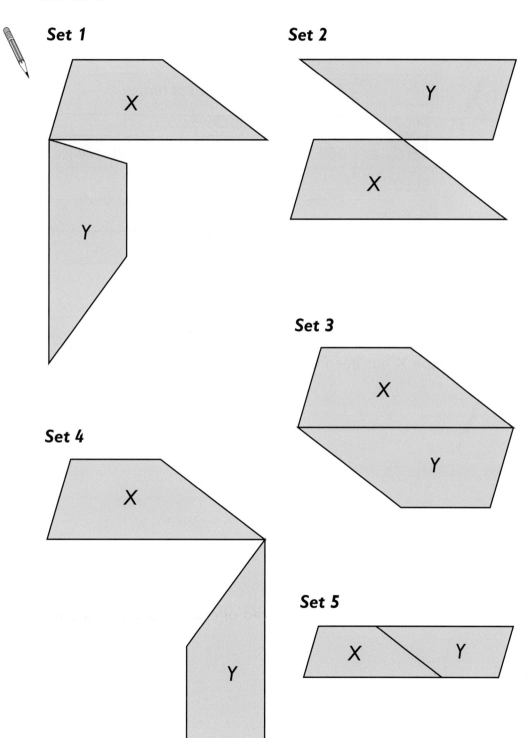

Set 1

Set 2

Set 3

Set 4

Set 5

2

TOTAL

2

In Set 1, we can say that Shape X has been rotated **clockwise** through an angle of **90°** onto Shape Y.

In Set 2, Shape X has been rotated **clockwise or anticlockwise** through an angle of **180°** onto Shape Y.

This information is shown in the table below.

b Complete the table.

	Angle	Direction of turn
Set 1	90°	clockwise
Set 2	180°	clockwise or anticlockwise
Set 3		
Set 4		
Set 5		

2

c Explain in your own words why for Set 2 we can say that Shape X has been turned either clockwise **or** anticlockwise.

1

TOTAL

3

26

2 Shape A is a rectangle. Its **length** is **twice** its **width**.

Six of Shape A are joined together to make Shape B.

Shape A

Shape B

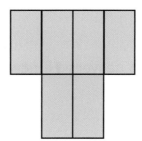

a Write an expression, using *n*, to show the **perimeter** of Shape A.
Give your answer in its simplest form.

....

1

b Write an expression, using *n*, to show the **perimeter** of Shape B. Give your answer in its simplest form.

....

1

c If the perimeter of **Shape B** is **80 cm**, calculate the perimeter of Shape A in centimetres.

Perimeter of Shape A = ... cm

1

TOTAL

3

27

Newspapers

3 Alan and Clive deliver newspapers.

Alan delivers **3** newspapers for every
2 newspapers that Clive delivers.

a If **Alan** delivers **18** newspapers, how many does **Clive**
deliver?

1

b If **Clive** delivers **24** newspapers, how many does **Alan**
deliver?

1

c If they deliver a **total** of **80** newspapers altogether, how
many do they each deliver?

1

Alan delivers .... Clive delivers ....

TOTAL

3

4   Jane buys a net of a gift box.

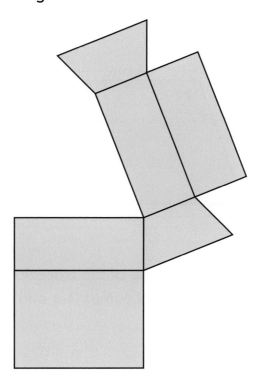

a   One of these pictures shows the box that Jane's net folds up to make.

Tick the correct picture.

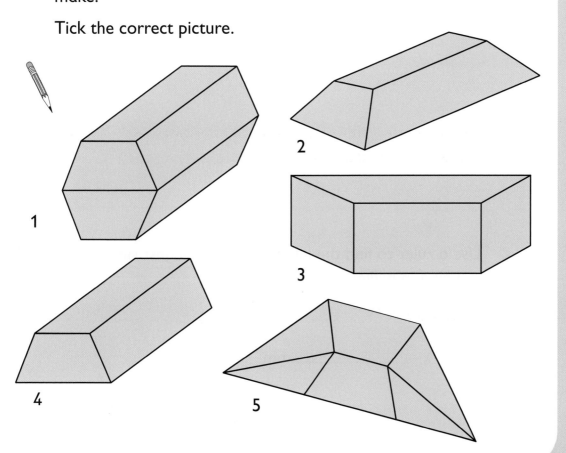

1

2

3

4

5

This sketch shows the measurements of one of the trapeziums of Jane's box. The length of the longest side is not given.

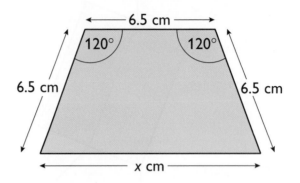

b Make an **accurate** drawing of the trapezium.
You may use a ruler, pair of compasses and a protractor.

2

c Use a ruler to find the length of *x*, the longest side of your drawing, in millimetres.

x = ... mm

1

TOTAL

3

5 a The number of people attending different football matches has been recorded in a table.

The attendance for the first match has been rounded to the nearest 100 and 1000.

Complete the table.

Teams	Attendance	Attendance to the nearest 100	Attendance to the nearest 1000
City v United	3685	3700	4000
Borough v City	3549		
Celtic v United	3462		

1

b For a different football match the attendance is **2000** when rounded to the nearest 1000 and is **1800** when rounded to the nearest 100.

Write a number to show how many people could have attended this match.

....

1

c For another football match the attendance is **0** when rounded to the nearest 1000 and **500** when rounded to the nearest 100.

Give the **largest** and **smallest** number of people that could have attended this match.

   Largest ....   Smallest ....

2

TOTAL

4

Exchange rates

6 The exchange rates for different countries are shown below.

> **£1 = 1.80 US dollars**
>
> **£1 = 450 Hungarian forint**

a Use the exchange rates above to find how much 85p is in US dollars. You must show your working.

85p = ... US dollars

2

b Use the exchange rates above to find how much 765 Hungarian forint are in pounds. You must show your working.

765 Hungarian forint = £ ....

2

c Use the exchange rates above to find how much **1 US dollar** is in **Hungarian forint**. You must show your working.

1 US dollar = ... Hungarian forint

2

TOTAL

6

7 Alisha has made two cuboids from cubes. Two of the cubes are coloured.

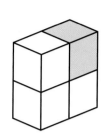 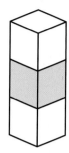

Alisha joins the two cuboids together to make a shape.

Here is a picture of one shape she could make:

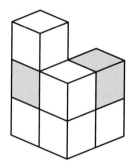

a Sketch a picture of a different shape she could make.

Shade the two coloured cubes on your picture.

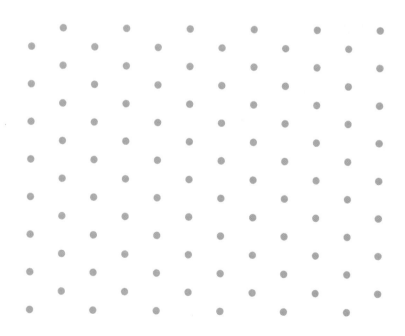

2

TOTAL

2

Alisha looks closely at this shape from six different angles.
She looks from **above**, from **all four sides** and from **below**.
She draws the view from each angle.

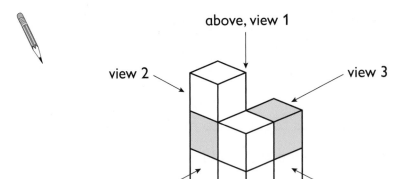

above, view 1

view 2

view 3

view 4

view 5

below, view 6

b Alisha's drawings are not in order. Write the number next to each drawing to show which view each is.

One has been done for you.

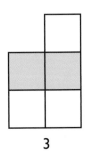

3

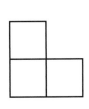

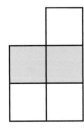

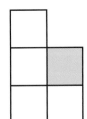

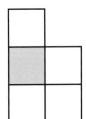

2

8 Two baskets contain boxes showing different expressions.

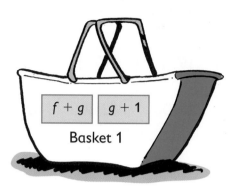

Basket 1

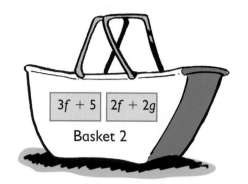

Basket 2

The boxes in **Basket 1** can be **added** to make the expression

$$f + 2g + 1$$

a Write an expression by adding the boxes in **Basket 2**.

Give your expression in its simplest form.

1

b Write an expression by adding together all the boxes in **Basket 1** and **Basket 2**. Give your expression in its simplest form.

1

c Explain why the total of **Basket 1** and **Basket 2** (your answer to part b) must always be an **even** number.

1

TOTAL

3

9 The average number of motor vehicles per day on motorways during 1981, 1991 and 1996 is shown below.

	1981	1991	1996
Average number of motor vehicles per day	30 400	53 800	62 400

a If **12%** of the motor vehicles travelling in **1981** were lorries, calculate the average number of lorries per day.

1

b There was a **7.5% increase** in the figures from **1996** to **1998**.

Calculate the average number of motor vehicles per day in **1998**.

Show your working.

2

c Calculate the **percentage increase** in the figures from **1981** to **1996**.

Give your answer to the nearest whole number.

Show your working.

2

TOTAL

5

10 The diagonals of a square are 4.6 cm:

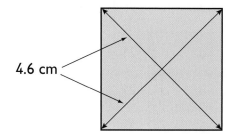

4.6 cm

a Calculate the **area** of this square.
You will *not* get a mark for answering this question by
drawing an accurate diagram. Show your working.

Area of square = ... cm²

2

b The square is cut in half along one
of its diagonals to make a triangle.
This triangle is identical to the end
face of a triangular prism which
has a length of 10 cm:

NOT TO SCALE

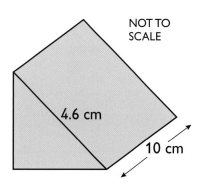
4.6 cm
10 cm

Calculate the volume of this triangular prism.
Show your working.

2

TOTAL

Volume of triangular prism = ... cm³

Squares

4

11 In this puzzle the letters a and b stand for numbers.

The totals for each row and column are given.

b	b	a	b	21 ⟶ b + b + a + b = 21
b	a	b	b	21
a	a	b	a	23
a	b	b	a	22

22 22 21 22

Using the puzzle, write two equations and use them to find the values of the letters a and b.

Show your working.

a = ...   b = ...

12 This diagram shows a picture of a CD lying on a rectangular piece of paper. The CD is a circular disk with a circular hole at its centre.

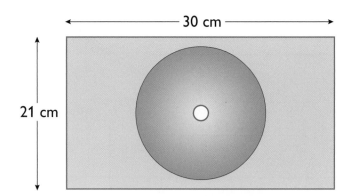

NOT TO SCALE

The **diameter** of the CD is **12 cm** and the **diameter** of the hole is **1.5 cm**. The piece of paper has a length of **30 cm** and a width of **21 cm**.

a Find the area of the piece of paper that is *not* covered by the CD.

Show your working. Take π to be 3.14.

Give your answer to 2 decimal places.

.... cm^2

3

TOTAL

3

Saba draws a line around the outside of the CD. Her line is exactly 2 mm from the circumference of the CD.

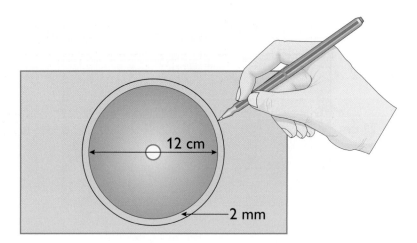

12 cm

2 mm

b Assuming Saba's line is an exact circle, calculate the difference between the length of her line and the true circumference of the CD.

Give your answer to the nearest millimetre.

2

c The CD has a thickness of 1 mm. Find the volume of the CD.

Give your answer in centimetres cubed (cm³) to 3 decimal places.

2

TOTAL

4

13 This simplified graph shows the journey of a car travelling from Sheffield to London, via Birmingham.

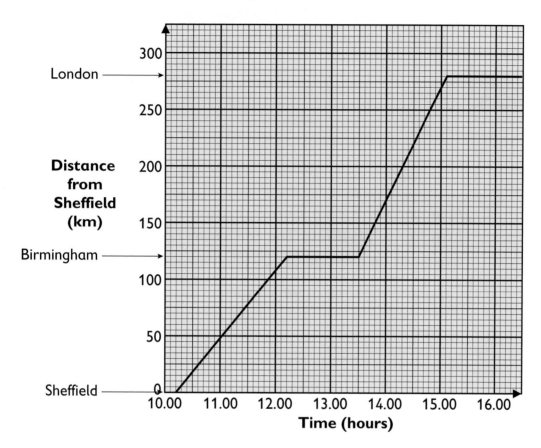

a Find the car's average speed between Sheffield and Birmingham.

.... km/h

b Look at the graph. Without calculating, say whether you think the average speed between Birmingham and London is **greater** or **less** than the average speed between Sheffield and Birmingham. Explain your answer.

1

c A second car is on a journey. It travels directly from **London** to **Sheffield**. The car leaves London at 13.06 and travels at an average of 100 kilometres per hour (km/h).

Calculate the time at which the car arrives in Sheffield.

2

d Draw a line on the graph to show the second car's journey.

At one point on their journeys the two cars are the same distance from Sheffield. What is this distance?

1

.... km

TOTAL

4

14

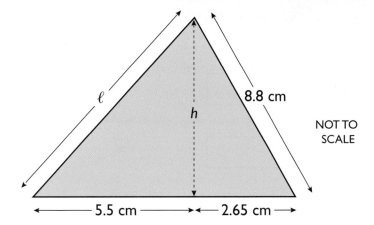

ℓ

h

8.8 cm

NOT TO
SCALE

5.5 cm — 2.65 cm

a Find the perpendicular height (*h*) of this triangle.

Give your answer to 3 significant figures.

2

b Use your answer to part (a) to calculate the length of side ℓ.

Give your answer to 3 significant figures.

2

TOTAL

4

5-second questions

1 ⬜

1

2 ⬜

1

3 ⬜

1

4 ⬜

1

5 ⬜ $\dfrac{1}{52}$

1

6 ⬜ $n + n + n$

1

10-second questions

7 ⬜

1

8 ⬜

1

9 ⬜ degrees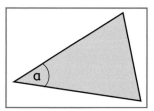

1

10 ⬜ %

1

TOTAL

10

| 11 | | $3y - 1$ |

1

| 12 | | 5.36 |

1

| 13 | | feet |

1

| 14 | | $4b = 24$ |

1

| 15 | |

1

| 16 | | 0.025 cm 0.25 cm 2.5 cm 25 cm |

1

| 17 | | $\dfrac{3}{8}$ |

1

| 18 | cm^2 |

8 cm

15 cm

1

15-second questions

| 19 | |

1

| 20 | cm |

6 cm

8 cm

1

TOTAL

10

| 21 | and | 3 40 |

| 22 | |

| 23 | | 147.34 ÷ 5.2 |

| 24 | | maths test scores
8 5 2 2 3 |

| 25 | m |

| 26 | feet |

| 27 | | 3.6 3.45 3.78 3.8 |

| 28 | | 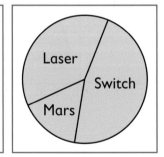 |

| 29 | £ |

| 30 | |

1
1
1
1
1
1
1
1
1
1

TOTAL

10

"For this first set of questions you have five seconds to work out each answer and write it down."

1 What is two hundred multiplied by ten?

2 How many centimetres are there in four metres?

3 Write one-fifth as a decimal.

4 Four times a number is six. What is the number?

5 The probability that I pick the two of clubs from a pack of playing cards is one out of fifty-two. What is the probability that I don't pick the two of clubs?

6 Simplify the expression on the answer sheet into its simplest form.

"For the next set of questions you have ten seconds to work out each answer and write it down."

7 Add seven point six to five point eight.

8 What is twenty per cent of fifty?

9 Look at the answer sheet. Estimate the size of angle *a* in degrees.

10 Three out of twenty apples in a box were rotten. What percentage were rotten?

11 Look at the answer sheet. What is the value of the expression when *y* equals seven?

12 Write two numbers that add up to five point three six.

13 A room is six metres long. About how many feet long is the room?

14 Look at the answer sheet. What is the value of seven *b*?

15 The probability that a football match will end in a draw is nought point four. If fifty matches are played, how many do you think will be drawn ?

16 Look at the answer sheet. Which measurement is about the same as one inch?

17 Write a fraction that is equivalent to three-eighths.

18 Look at the answer sheet. What is the area of the parallelogram?

"For the next set of questions you have fifteen seconds to work out each answer and write it down."

19 Write three even numbers that add up to thirty-two.

20 Look at the answer sheet. What is the length of the missing side?

21 The difference between m and n is three. The product of m and n is forty. What are the values of m and n?

22 Multiply twenty-five by twenty-four.

23 Look at the answer sheet. Write an approximate answer to the question.

24 Look at the answer sheet. Write the mean number of the scores given.

25 The circumference of a circular lawn is twenty-four metres. What is the approximate diameter of the lawn?

26 Divide a length of rope which is thirty-eight feet long into four equal lengths.

27 Look at the answer sheet. Draw a ring around the largest number.

28 Look at the answer sheet. Forty people visited a theme park. The pie chart shows which ride they preferred. About how many people preferred the Laser?

29 A magazine costs two pounds ninety-nine. What would six magazines cost?

30 There are twenty-four chocolates in a box. There are three times as many milk chocolates as dark chocolates. How many milk chocolates are there?

Question number	Answer	Mark	Comments and tips
Practice questions	209 595 33 Two numbers that make the equation true (eg. 400, 2)	–	You cannot use calculators for <u>any</u> of the questions in Paper 1. You can work answers out anywhere on the page or you can work answers out mentally. For some questions you might gain a mark for your written working out even if you get the answer wrong.
What's missing			
1a	100	1	Always look at the finished equation when you have written a missing number to see if it makes sense. For the question ☐ − 40 = 87, if you <u>incorrectly</u> took away 40 from 87 and wrote the missing number $\boxed{47}$, you can see that **47 − 40** doesn't equal 87!
1b	4	1	
1c	127	1	
1d	30	1	
1e	Two numbers that make the equation true (eg. 24, 2).	1	
Ice-skating			
2a	4.9, 5.5, 5.6, 5.8, 6.0	1	The numbers must be in this order to get a mark.
2b	27.8	1	
2c	Any number that lies between 5.5 and 5.6, i.e. a number with 3 or more digits starting with 5.5 e.g. 5.51, 5.59, 5.5345 etc.	1	
2d	254	1	When multiplying numbers or decimals by 10, the digits move across one column to the left. For 25.4 × 10, the 2 tens become 2 hundreds, the 5 units become 5 tens and the 4 tenths become 4 units, giving the answer 254.
Fractions and percentages			
3a	$\frac{3}{10}$	1	The line is divided into ten equal parts (the number on the bottom of your fraction) and the snail has moved along 3 parts (the number on the top).
3b	$\frac{3}{5}$	1	This question specifies giving your answer in its simplest form. Snail B has moved six tenths of the way along. $\frac{6}{10} = \frac{3}{5}$ To simplify fractions cancel the top and bottom numbers by the same number, in this case by 2.
3c	20%	1	Two tenths as a percentage is 20%. If you think of the whole line as 100%, each part is one tenth (10%) so two parts are 20%.
3d	A mark should be made two tenths of the way along.	1	1 Snail B has travelled along 6 parts. $\frac{1}{3}$ of 6 can be found by splitting 6 into 3 equal parts = 2 parts.
3e	An arrow three-fifths of the way along the line.	1	The line can be divided into 5 equal parts and the arrow should go at the end of the third part.

Question number	Answer	Mark	Comments and tips
Shopping			
4a	£15 or £15.00	1	Note that amounts should never be written with both the **£** sign and a **p** sign, e.g. £15.00p is wrong.
4b	£13.47	1	
4c	2 pairs	1	He must have bought $2 \times £1.25 = £2.50$ and $2 \times £4.49 = £8.98$, which is a total of £11.48
4d	£8.52	1	To check an answer like this while sitting the paper, try adding the amount Dave spends to the answer you have written. It should come to £20.
4e	T-shirts socks 4 1 3 5 2 8 1 12	1	With each combination of T-shirts and socks Jennie will have some change left over, but she can only afford a maximum of 4 T-shirts.
Tiles			
5(a–d)	Two different shapes made from two tiles, e.g. and the perimeters given in centimetres.	4	The perimeter of a shape is the distance all the way around the edge. Here are examples of the perimeters for the shapes shown.
Pick a card			
6a	$\frac{1}{10}$	1	There are 10 cards. The probability of picking the four of diamonds is one out of ten. Probabilities generally can be written as fractions or decimals, e.g. $\frac{1}{4}$ **or 0.25**
6b		1	There are 10 cards. The probability of picking the eight of diamonds is one out of ten. Note that $\frac{1}{10}$ can be marked on the line by splitting the whole line into 10 equal parts.
6c		1	There are 10 cards. The probability of picking a number less than 5 (1, 2, 3 or 4) is four out of ten. Note that $\frac{4}{10}$ is the same as $\frac{2}{5}$.
6d	Your explanation should include the idea that tests are not always reliable. James only tried it 50 times. The probability of picking a 5 is still one-tenth.	1	The greater the number of tests carried, out the more likely the results will match the theoretical probability.
Grid game			
7a	4 and −1	1	
7b	4 and −6, or −2 and 0	1	Either answer can be given. Note that 8 and −6 = 2 not −2.
7c	8 and −6 4 and −2	2	1 mark is given for each.

Question number	Answer	Mark	Comments and tips
Symmetry			
8	Shape B 2 2 Shape C 1 1 Shape D 0 1 Shape E 0 2	4	I mark is given for each shape. People often make the mistake of thinking that a parallelogram (Shape E) has reflective symmetry. Cut out a copy of Shape E and try folding it to see!
Purse problems			
9a	$n - 10$	1	Do not write $n - 10\mathbf{p}$. The expression shows how many pence there are: you do not need to write it again.
9b	$n \div 2$ or $\frac{1}{2}n$ or $\frac{n}{2}$	1	Any of these three expressions are acceptable, but the second two are preferable.
9c	$100n$	1	The answers $n \times 100$ or $100 \times n$ are acceptable, but it is better to shorten the expression to $100n$.
9d	n	1	Clare's mum has $100n$ in pence, so she has 100 times fewer pounds, in other words n pounds.
9e	The wallets hold the same amount. Your explanation should show that for $2(n + 2)$, when the brackets are removed the expression becomes $2n + 4$.	1	When removing brackets you must multiply whatever is outside the brackets by <u>everything</u> inside the brackets. People sometimes forget and only multiply the first number in the brackets. $2(n + 2)$ does NOT equal $2n + 2$, but equals $2n + \mathbf{4}$.
Running			
10a	$13\frac{3}{4}$ or approximately 14 hours. You only get <u>one</u> mark for the answer 13.	2	One mark is given for dividing 220 by 16. The other mark is given for interpreting your answer and realising that it is more than just 13 hours.
10b	60	1	Any mental or written method for getting this answer is acceptable, e.g. $(16 \times 3) +$ (three quarters of 16) $= 48 + 12 = 60$
10c	10 miles	1	You should memorise the fact that 1 mile is approximately 1.6 km. Therefore 16 km is approximately 10 miles.
Angles			
11	$a = 95°$ $b = 85°$ $c = 35°$	3	Angle a is found by subtracting $85°$ from $180°$ (angles on a straight line). Angle b is the same as the $85°$ angle as there are 2 parallel lines with the line RS crossing both of them. Imagine the $85°$ angle sliding along line RS until it sits on top of angle b. You will see that they are the same. Angle c is an angle inside an isosceles triangle (where 2 sides and 2 angles are the same). If one of the angles is $110°$, then c and the other angle must add up to $70°$, since the angles inside a triangle add to $180°$. The other angle is the same as c so c must be half of $70° = 35°$.

Paper 1 Answers

Question number	Answer	Mark	Comments and tips
Sequences			
12a	10 12 32 40 1 mark for each correct row.	2	The number of coloured squares is always 2 more than the shape number. The number of white squares is always 4 times the shape number.
12b	$n + 2$ or $2 + n$ $4n$ or $n \times 4$ or $4 \times n$ 1 mark for each correct row.	2	The number of coloured squares is always 2 more than the shape number (n). The number of white squares is always 4 times the shape number (n).
12c	$5n + 2$ or $2 + 5n$	1	$n + 2 + 4n = 5n + 2$
12d	Set 2	1	A tip for finding the correct set in a question of this type is to look at the number multiplied by n, in this case 4. Look for the set of shapes which grows by 4 each time.
Linear equations			
13a	The horizontal side of the pentagon $y = 4$ drawn in bold.	1	Lines with the equation $y = $ 'a number' are horizontal. Lines with the equation $x = $ 'a number' are vertical. Lines with an equation with x and y are diagonal.
13b	$y = \frac{1}{2}x$ or $y = \frac{1}{2}x + 0$	1	In the general equation $y = mx + c$, m stands for the gradient. For this line the gradient (slope) is the same as the longest side which is given as HALF. The c stands for the point at which the line would cross the y axis. The longest side crosses at 4. The line you are finding would cross at zero.
Probability			
14a	$\frac{12}{20}, \frac{6}{10}, 0.6, 60\%, \frac{3}{5}$	2	1 mark given for three or four correct. 2 marks given for five correct
14b	$\frac{13}{20}$	1	Thirteen out of the twenty children do not have a name beginning with the letter S.
14c	65%	1	$\frac{13}{20}$ is equivalent to $\frac{65}{100}$ which is 65%.
Areas			
15a	3.5 cm or $3\frac{1}{2}$ cm	2	1 mark given for using the equation area $= \frac{(a + b)}{2} \times h$ even if answer is incorrect. The area of the parallelogram is 9 cm^2 and the area of the trapezium is therefore 18 cm^2. $18 = \frac{(a + 8.5)}{2} \times 3$ Divide 18 by 3 to get 6. $6 = \frac{(a + 8.5)}{2}$ Multiply 6 by 2 to get 12. $12 = a + 8.5$, therefore a must be 3.5 cm.
15b	Area $= 6b^2$	1	Area $= \frac{(b + 3b)}{2} \times 3b$ $= \frac{4b}{2} \times 3b = 2b \times 3b = 6b^2$

You **can** use calculators for <u>any</u> of the questions in Paper 2.

Question number	Answers	Marks	Comments and tips
Rotation			
1a		2	2 marks for all five crosses correctly positioned. 1 mark for four correctly positioned.
1b	Set 3: 180° clockwise or anticlockwise Set 4: 90° anticlockwise or 270° clockwise Set 5: 180° clockwise or anticlockwise	2	1 mark is given if only 2 out of 3 answers are correct. Rotations can be performed in a clockwise or anticlockwise direction. For angles other than 180° the direction you specify is vital, e.g. 90° clockwise is not the same as 90° anticlockwise.
1c	Your explanation should show that you realise that rotating a shape 180° clockwise results in the same image as if rotated anticlockwise.	1	
Perimeters			
2a	$6n$	1	The perimeter of a shape is the distance all the way around the edge. Here the perimeter is $2n + n + 2n + n = 6n$.
2b	$16n$	1	The perimeter of a shape is the distance all the way around the edge. Here the perimeter is 8 short sides ($n \times 8$) plus four longer sides ($2n \times 4$) which equals $16n$ in total.
2c	30 cm	1	If the perimeter of the larger shape ($16n$) is 80cm, divide 80 by 16 to find n. $80 \div 16 = 5$, therefore $n = 5$. To find the perimeter of Shape A ($6n$) we know that $n = 5$, so $6n = 30$.
Newspapers			
3a	12	1	Alan delivers 3 for every 2 that Clive delivers. We can write this as the ratio 3 : 2. If Alan delivers 18 (six times his number in the ratio) then Clive must deliver six times <u>his</u> number in the ratio, i.e. $6 \times 2 = 12$.
3b	36	1	Using the ratio 3 : 2, if Clive delivers 24 (twelve times his number in the ratio) then Alan must deliver twelve times <u>his</u> number in the ratio, i.e. $12 \times 3 = 36$.
3c	48 and 32	1	In the ratio 3 : 2, there are a total of 5 parts. If a total of 80 papers are delivered (sixteen times the ratio total) then Alan and Clive both must deliver sixteen times their numbers in the ratio.

Paper 2 Answers

Question number	Answer	Mark	Comments and tips
Gift box			
4a	4	1	
4b and c	An accurate drawing of the trapezium with side x measuring 130 mm exactly	3	2 marks only for parts b and c together can be given if the answer to part c is within the range 128 mm to 132 mm.
Rounding			
5a	3500 4000 3500 3000	1	All must be correct to get a mark.
5b	A number between 1750 and 1849.	1	Numbers ending in 5, 50 and 500 generally are rounded up rather than down when rounded to the nearest 10, 100 and 1000 respectively.
5c	Largest = 499 Smallest = 450 1 mark for each.	2	If the number was above 499, i.e. 500, it would round to 1000, to the nearest 1000. If the number was below 450, i.e. 449 it would round to 400 to the nearest 100.
Exchange rates			
6a	1.53	2	Divide 1.80 US dollars by 100 to find how many dollars are the same as 1 pence. Then multiply by 85.
6b	£1.70 You do *not* get an answer for writing 1.7 or £1.7.	2	Divide 765 forints by 450 to find how many pounds they are equivalent to.
6c	250	2	Divide 450 forints by 1.80 to find how many forints are equivalent to one dollar.
Cubes			
7a	An accurate drawing of a shape made from the two cuboids.	2	The two coloured cubes must be shaded to get both marks.
7b	3 6 2 5 4 1 1 mark only if two are incorrect.	2	
Expressions			
8a	$5f + 2g + 5$	1	For the expression to be in its simplest form the like terms should be collected.
8b	$6f + 4g + 6$	1	
8c	Your explanation should show how you can tell that the expression is even, preferably by showing that $2(3f + 2g + 3)$ is the same as the expression.	1	Be careful not to just repeat the question in your answer, e.g. by saying "It is even" without proving it. If a number is even it is a multiple of 2 and we can see this is a multiple of 2 by factorising, creating the expression $2(3f + 2g + 3)$.

Question number	Answer	Mark	Comments and tips
Percentages			
9a	3648	1	30 400 × 12 ÷ 100
9b	67 080 1 mark if your working includes the number 4680 with an incorrect final answer.	2	62 400 × 7.5 ÷ 100 = 4680 This is the amount it is increased by, therefore 1998's figures are 62 400 + 4680 = 67 080.
9c	105% 1 mark if your answer is 105.263 (not rounded to the nearest whole number).	2	62 400 − 30 400 = 32 000 gives the increased amount. To find the percentage: 32 000 (increase) ÷ 30 400 (original amount) × 100 = 105.263. The answer must be to the nearest whole number.
Squares			
10a	10.58 cm^2	2	There are several ways of answering this question. The simplest way is to look at the square as four right-angled triangles. The four triangles must have sides of 2.3 (half of 4.6) and so the area of one triangle is $\frac{1}{2} \times 2.3 \times 2.3$. Multiply this answer by 4 to find the area of the square. A second method (if confident) is to use Pythagoras' Theorem ($a^2 + b^2 = c^2$) for one of these triangles. This can help you to find the length of one side of the square or, better still, this length squared (the area) e.g. $2.3^2 + 2.3^2 = c^2$. c^2 is the same as the area as c is one side of the square.
10b	52.9 cm^3 If your answer to part a is wrong you can get 1 mark if you have worked out this answer by dividing your answer to part a by 2 and multiplying by 10.	2	To find the volume, multiply the area of the end face by the length, i.e. area of triangle = half the area of the square (part a) × 10: 10.58 ÷ 2 × 10.
Puzzles			
11	$a = 6$ $b = 5$ 1 mark for two of these equations shown: $3b + a = 21$ $3a + b = 23$ $2a + 2b = 22$ 2 marks for getting the answer to either a or b (but not both) correct.	3	There are different methods for solving simultaneous equations, including the substitution method of which an example is shown below: Halve each value in $2a + 2b = 22$ to give the equation $a + b = 11$ If $a + b = 11$ then $a = 11 - b$ Substitute $11 - b$ for a in the equation $3b + a = 21$ $3b + (11 - b) = 21$, therefore $2b + 11 = 21$, and $2b = 10$, so b must equal 5. This can be inserted into the equation $a + b = 11$, to show that $a = 6$.

Question number	Answer	Mark	Comments and tips
CD problems			
12a	518.73 cm^2 2 marks if your answer is not rounded to 2 decimal places. 1 mark if you have the wrong final answer but have correctly found the area of the CD as 111.27 cm^2. Only 2 marks given for the answer 518.67 cm^2 (use of π button on calculator)	3	To find the area of the paper not covered by the CD first find the area of the CD: Area of a circle = πr^2 Area of CD circle (including the hole) = $\pi \times 6^2$ = 113.04 cm^2 Area of the inner circle (hole) = $\pi \times 0.75^2$ = 1.77 cm^2 Subtract hole from CD circle = 113.04 − 1.77 = 111.27 cm^2. This is the area of the CD. The area of the paper = 30 cm $\times$ 21 cm = 630 cm^2 Now subtract 111.27 from 630 = 518.73 cm^2 NOTE: *If you have used the π button on your calculator your answers will be different. The question stated that π should be taken as 3.14.*
12b	1.3 cm or 13 mm 1 mark for the answer 1.256 cm or 1.2566 cm.	2	Circumference = $2\pi r$ or πd Circumference of CD = 12 $\times$ π = 37.68 (if π = 3.14) Length of Saba's line = 12.4 $\times$ π = 38.936 (if π = 3.14) so for the difference: 38.936 − 37.68 = 1.256
12c	11.127 cm^3 1 mark if your answer is one tenth of the value of the area of the CD calculated in part a.	2	The thickness is given in millimetres and should be converted to centimetres, e.g. 1 mm = 0.1 cm. The volume is length (thickness) multiplied by the area of the end face, i.e. the area of the CD.
Journeys			
13a	60 km/h	1	The car travels 120 km in two hours, so 60 km in one hour.
13b	Greater Your answer must show that you've noticed that the gradient (slope) is steeper for the second part of the journey.	1	The steeper the gradient, the faster the speed: in other words, the car travels more km in a shorter time.
13c	15.54 1 mark for the number 2.8 in your working.	2	It would take the car 2.8 hours. This is found by dividing 280 km by 100 km/h. 0.8 hours is 48 minutes. This can be found by multiplying 0.8 $\times$ 60 = 48. So the journey would take 2 hours and 48 minutes.
13d	180 km	1	The point where your two lines should cross.
Triangles			
14a	8.39 cm 1 mark if your answer has more than 3 digits, e.g. 8.392 or 8.3915...	2	Use Pythagoras' Theorem ($a^2 + b^2 = c^2$). $2.65^2 + h^2 = 8.8^2$ so $h^2 = 8.8^2 - 2.65^2$ $h^2 = 70.4175$, therefore h = 8.3915 cm
14b	10.0 cm 1 mark if your answer has more than 3 digits, e.g. 10.03 or 10.032.	2	Use your answer to part a and Pythagoras' Theorem ($a^2 + b^2 = c^2$). $8.39^2 + 5.5^2 = \ell^2$ $\ell^2 = 100.6421$, therefore ℓ = 10.03205 cm

1	2000	16	2.5 cm
2	400	17	any fraction equivalent to $\frac{3}{8}$ e.g. $\frac{6}{16}$
3	0.2 or .2	18	120 cm²
4	1.5 or $1\frac{1}{2}$	19	three even numbers that add up to 32 e.g. 20, 8, 4
5	$\frac{51}{52}$	20	10 cm
6	$3n$	21	8 and 5
7	13.4	22	600
8	10	23	approx 30
9	approx 40° (accept 35° – 45°)	24	4
10	15%	25	approx 7.5 m (accept 7.5-8.5)
11	20	26	9.5 feet
12	any two numbers that add up to 5.36 e.g. 5.1 + 0.26	27	3.8
13	approx 19.5 feet (accept 18 – 21 feet)	28	approx 15 (accept between 13 and 17)
14	42	29	£17.94
15	20	30	18

Allow one mark per answer.

National Curriculum Levels

Mark scored in Paper 1   [ ]   out of 62

Mark scored in Paper 2   [ ]   out of 60

Mark scored in Mental Maths Test   [ ]   out of 30

Total score   [ ]   out of 152

Use this table to find what level you might be working at.

Mark	0–20	21–40	41–80	81–120	121–140	141–152
Level	Level 3	Level 4	Level 5	Level 6	Level 7	Level 8

If you scored over 140 marks, you could try the Level 8 Extension Paper on the next page.

If you need more help with any Maths topics, try the WHSmith Key Stage 3 Maths Revision Guide.

1 <u>**Do NOT use a calculator for this question.**</u>

a Put a tick by the correct statement.

5×10^3 is smaller than 5^3 ....

5×10^3 is the same size as 5^3 ....

5×10^3 is larger than 5^3 ....

Explain your answer.

1

b Circle the number with the same value as 2.4×10^4

$(2.4 \times 10)^4$ 0.24×10^3 24^4 24^3

0.24×10^4 240×10^2 2400×10^2

1

c Circle the number with the same value as 7.5×10^{-5}

7.5×10^{-4} 0.75×10^{-4} -75^5 75^{-5}

-0.75×10^4 0.0075×10^2 $75\,000 \times 10^2$

1

TOTAL

3

d Simplify these expressions. One has been done for you.

$$(2 \times 10^4) \times (4 \times 10^4) = \mathbf{8 \times 10^8}$$

$$(2 \times 10^{-4}) \times (4 \times 10^6) =$$

1

$$\frac{(4 \times 10^{10})}{(2 \times 10^2)} =$$

1

$$\frac{(8 \times 10^6)}{(2 \times 10^{-2})} =$$

1

2 <u>*You MAY use a calculator for this question.*</u>

Light travels at a speed of 300 000 km/s.

Express this speed in kilometres per hour.

Give your answer in standard form.

2

TOTAL

5

Answers

Extension Paper

1   a 5×10^3 is larger than 5^3.
       We can see that $5 \times 10^3 = 5000$ is larger than
       $5^3 = 125$.
   b 240×10^2
   c 0.75×10^{-4}
   d 8×10^2
       2×10^8
       4×10^8 *6 marks*

2   $300000 \times 60 \times 60 = 1.08 \times 10^9$ km/h   *2 marks*